Alphabet fun

Teachers' notes

Introduction

The activities in this book aim to provide the foundations for later learning in the National Curriculum and the Scottish 5–14 Guidelines. Before the age of five, children are not required to achieve any specific targets. Nevertheless, they are more likely to do so at the appropriate age if they have been accustomed to a learning environment that enables them to begin to understand some of the specific skills required for reading. Older children, who for some reason have missed out on these earlier learning opportunities, will also find these photocopiable worksheets helpful.

In themselves these worksheets are not a comprehensive programme. They are intended to support the many related activities to which teachers and parents introduce children from an early age. Day-to-day life exposes children to many opportunities for incidental learning. These worksheets help to formalise that learning, as well as providing practice in specific skills.

Completing the pages of *Alphabet fun* successfully will help to build the children's confidence and instil from a young age that learning is exciting and rewarding. Also, it will give the children tangible evidence that they are making progress.

Aim of this book

The main aim of this book of photocopiable worksheets is to familiarise young children with the *shapes* and *names* of all the letters of the alphabet. This is achieved by encouraging the children to look carefully at the letters, initially tracing over them with their fingers and then writing over them with pencils or highlighter pens. An adult helper should supply the letter names.

There is a variety of activities in this book which consolidate and reinforce this primary aim. The children should be encouraged to look closely at the details of the letters and, at all times, should be afforded opportunities to talk about the differences and similarities between the letters, such as which have tails above the line.

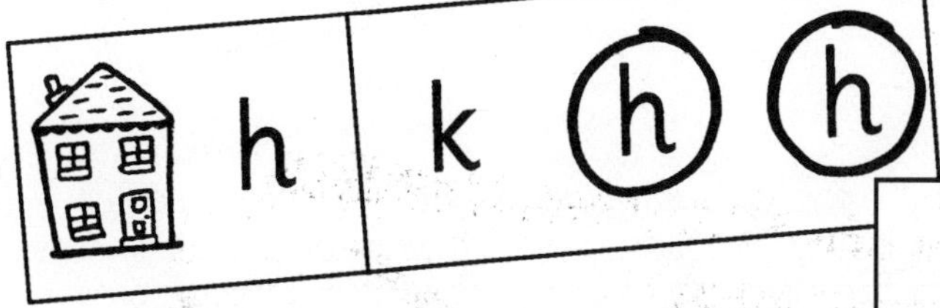

Although learning [illegible] the letters constitutes the most important objective of these worksheets, some of them also provide opportunities to talk about the letter *sounds*. However, children's auditory discrimination develops at varying rates – as a game of 'I-spy' in the classroom will confirm. So where the learning of this skill occurs, it is deliberately incidental so that it can easily be ignored if the children are not yet ready for this stage.

Wherever possible pictures have been included alongside the letters. As it is surprising what young children are able to absorb and quantify by association.

When the children have completed all the worksheets they will have been helped to learn how to:

- match letters;
- write letters;
- say the names of the letters;
- say the sounds of some letters.

Using the worksheets

Since the children who will be using these worksheets are very young they will not be able to read the instructions. However, it is absolutely essential that they fully understand what they have to do, so it is suggested that a teacher or a parent demonstrates the activity first. For this reason, no examples have been printed on the worksheets; it is so much more efficient to *do* this as the child watches. The child can then proceed independently.

When using these sheets it is important to remember:

- to make sure that the child understands the task;
- to always go over the finished pages together;
- to praise and encourage both effort and achievement;
- to let the children use a pencil first and then, perhaps, go over this with a felt-tipped pen;
- that some children will need more time than others.

Practical considerations

- Coloured paper can be used in the photocopier to provide an attractive alternative to plain white paper.

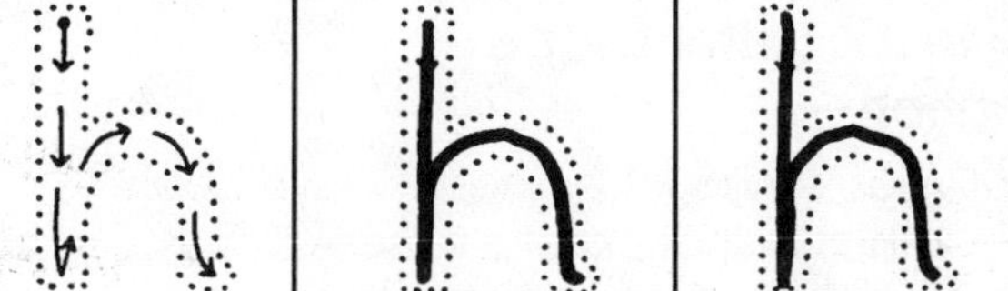

• Different writing implements can be used. Thick felt-tipped pens, with both solid and softer brush tips, help develop flowing writing movements. Chisel tips are much harder to use.
• The patterns on each sheet can be repeated several times at one sitting if the children are able to change their writing implements. Highlighter pens of various colours give young children much pleasure, even when they are repeating the same basic skill.
• The worksheets should rest on a soft surface, such as a magazine or clipboard, and not directly on a hard table.
• The worksheet should be positioned at an angle of 30° to 40° to the right (or left) of the child and not directly in front.
• The child's pencil grip should be comfortable and relaxed. Triangular grips may help those children whose grip is too tight.
• The children should be seated at a table which is of an appropriate height so that their feet touch the floor. Their arms and hands should rest on the paper.
• Left-handed children need space on their left-hand side and so should not be positioned to the right of another child.

Notes on individual activities

Pages 3 to 14: Recognising shapes of letters and writing them

These pages cover all the letters of the alphabet. The pages are paired so that there is the opportunity for the children to recognise the letter by using the first page and then practise writing it on the second page. On the first page of each pair, each letter shape has to be identified and circled. Pictures have been included for those children who show an interest in the sounds the letters make. On the second page, the letters for writing are deliberately large so that the children can trace them with their fingers before using pens.

Pages 15 to 18: Motor control and letter recognition

These are purposeful colouring activities. Pages 15 and 16 use two colours, while pages 17 and 18 use three. If the letters are correctly identified and coloured a picture appears.

Pages 19 to 21: Letter shape discrimination

In these activities, similar letter shapes have been grouped together so that careful observation is required to complete the task correctly.

Pages 22 to 27: Beginning letter shapes and sounds

The pictures can be matched by looking at the first letters of the words. Some children may match by the initial sounds, but it must be remembered that this is difficult for young children. These pages cover all the letters of the alphabet. For letters such as i, x and u there are a limited number of words and pictures that give the correct letter sound and are accessible to young children; hence some duplication becomes necessary.

Pages 28 to 32: Alphabetical order

Many teachers and parents help children to learn the alphabet by making it into a song. Consequently for these activities the alphabet has been divided into four segments to coincide with the rhythm of the most commonly used tune:

- abcdefg;
- hijklm;
- nopqrstu;
- vwxyz.

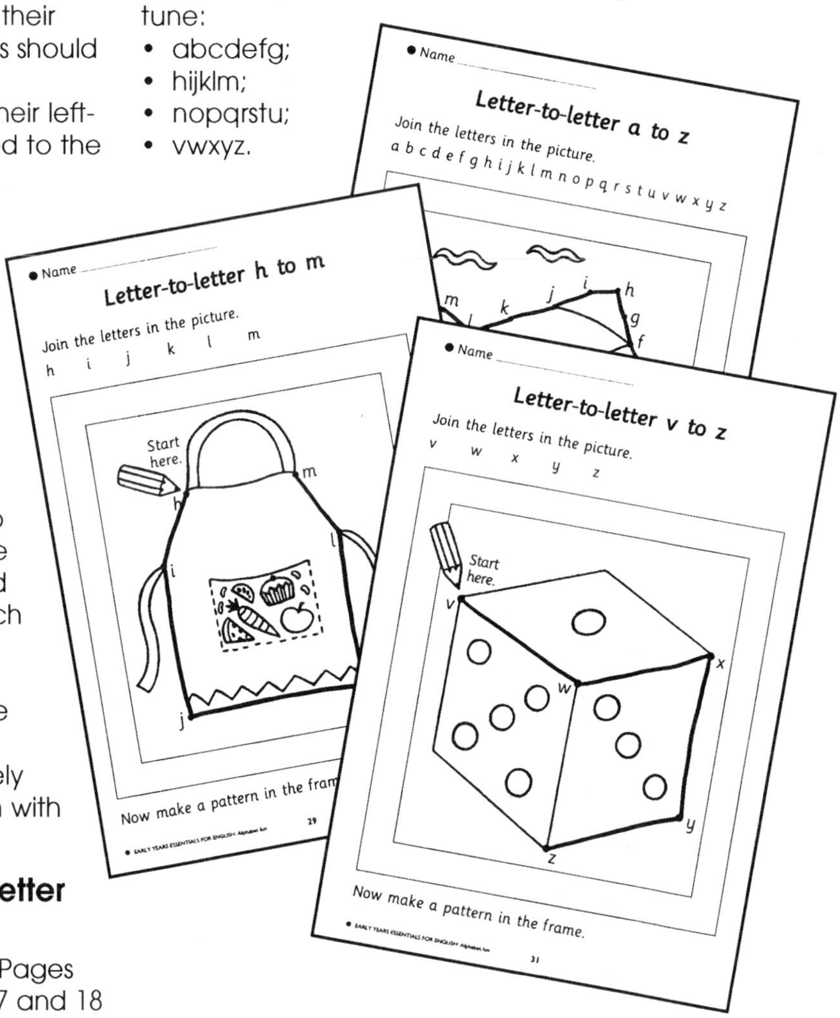

At the top of each page there is a reference sequence. This can always be covered up if you want to give the children a greater challenge.

Only some of the children will be able to complete the final page, as this uses *all* the letters of the alphabet.

● Name ___________________________

Letter shapes a to d

Look at the letter in the small box.

Draw a ring round those letters in the big box that look the same.

 a	a c a
 b	h b b
 c	c c e
 d	p d d

● Name ______________________

Writing a to d

Write each letter. Start at the dot.

a	a	a
b	b	b
c	c	c
d	d	d

● Name ___________________________

Letter shapes e to h

Look at the letter in the small box.

Draw a ring round those letters in the big box that look the same.

e	c e e
f	f l f
g	g g p
h	k h h

● Name ____________________

Writing e to h

Write each letter. Start at the dot.

e	e	e
f	f	f
g	g	g
h	h	h

Name ______________________

Letter shapes i to l

Look at the letter in the small box.

Draw a ring round those letters in the big box that look the same.

ink i	i	j	i
j	g	j	j
k	k	k	h
l	l	h	l

● Name ______________________________

Writing i to l

Write each letter. Start at the dot.

● Name ____________________

Letter shapes m to p

Look at the letter in the small box.
Draw a ring round those letters in the big box that look the same.

 m	m	m	w
 n	m	n	n
 o	o	u	o
 p	q	p	p

● Name ____________________

Writing m to p

Write each letter. Start at the dot.

m	m	m
n	n	n
o	o	o
p	p	p

● Name ______________________

Letter shapes q to u

Look at the letter in the small box.

Draw a ring round those letters in the big box that look the same.

 q	q g q
 r	n r r
 s	x s s
 t	t t l
 u	u u n

Name ______________________

Writing q to u

Write each letter. Start at the dot.

q	q	q
r	r	r
s	s	s
t	t	t
u	u	u

● Name ____________________

Letter shapes v to z

Look at the letter in the small box.
Draw a ring round those letters in the big box that look the same.

 v	v w v
 w	w v w
 x	z x x
 y	g y y
 z	z z x

Name ______________________

Writing v to z

Write each letter. Start at the dot.

v	v	v
w	w	w
x	x	x
y	y	y
z	z	z

● Name ____________________

Picture this – d and g

Colour the d spaces
Colour the g spaces

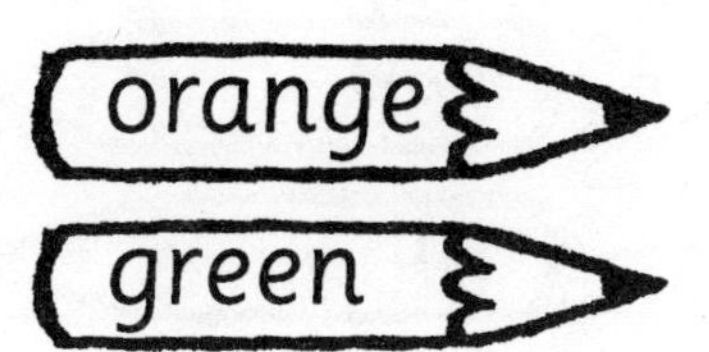

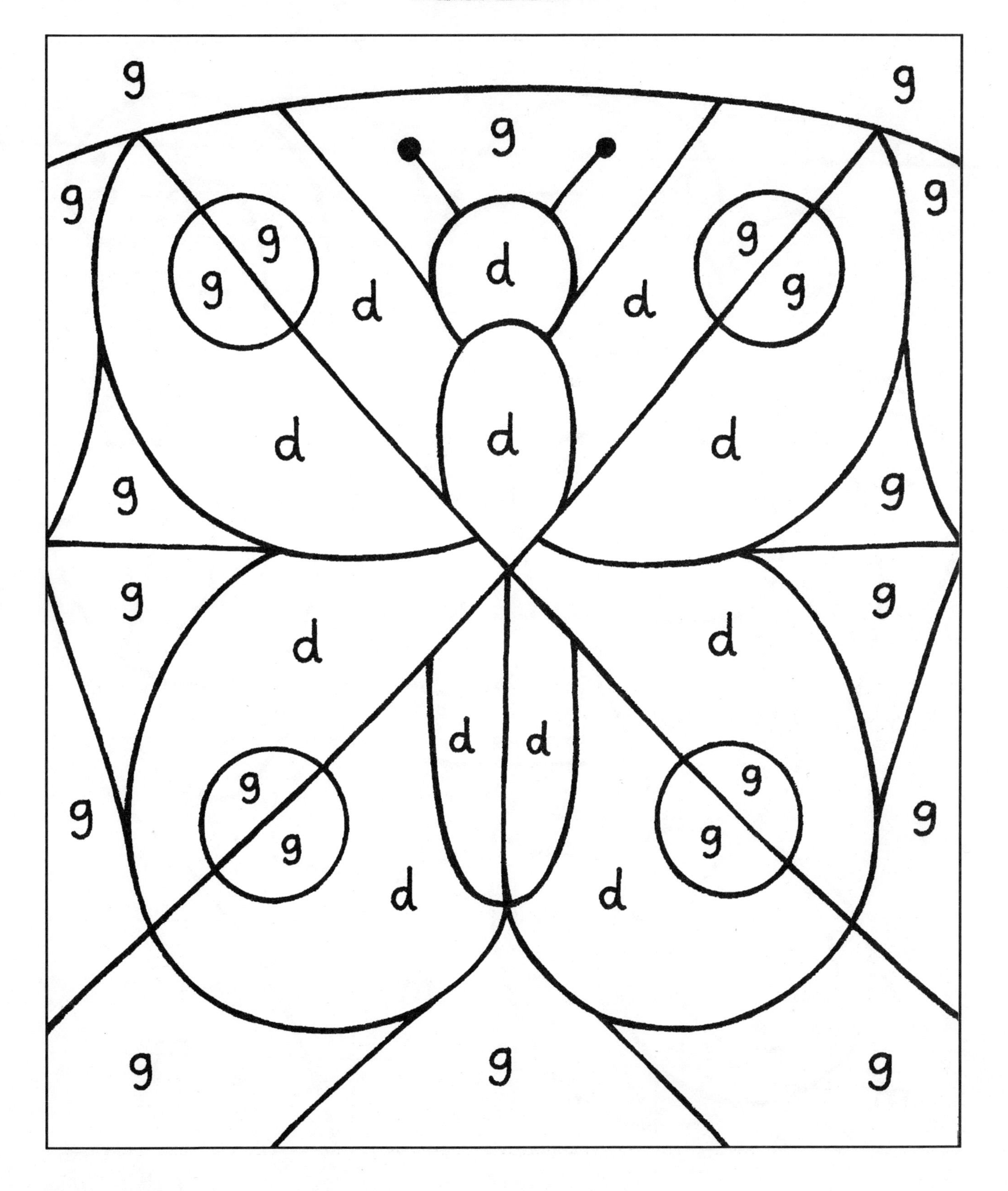

● Name ______________________

Picture this – m and s

Colour the m spaces 

Colour the s spaces

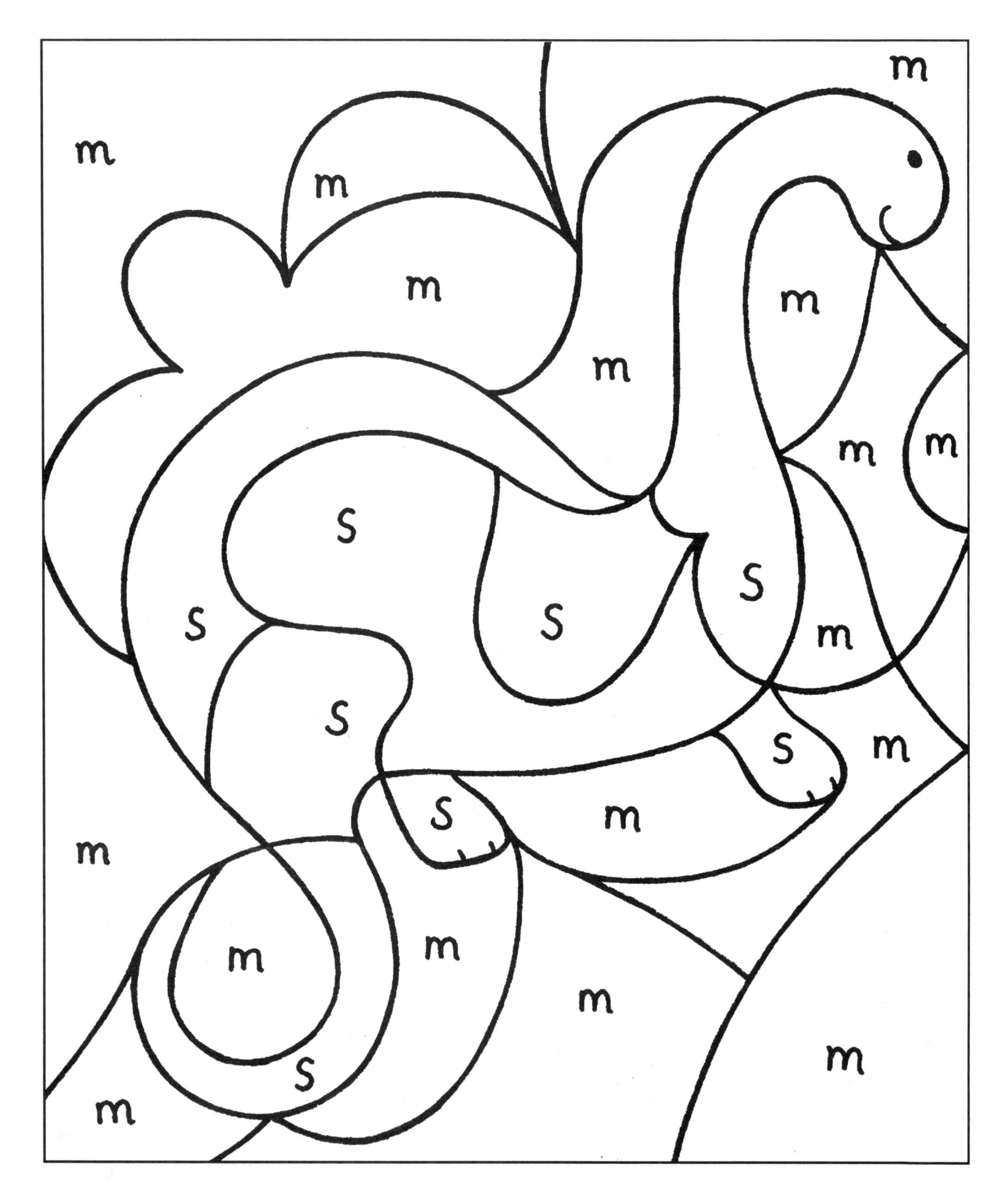

● Name ______________________

Picture this – o, h and b

Colour the o spaces

Colour the h spaces

Colour the b spaces

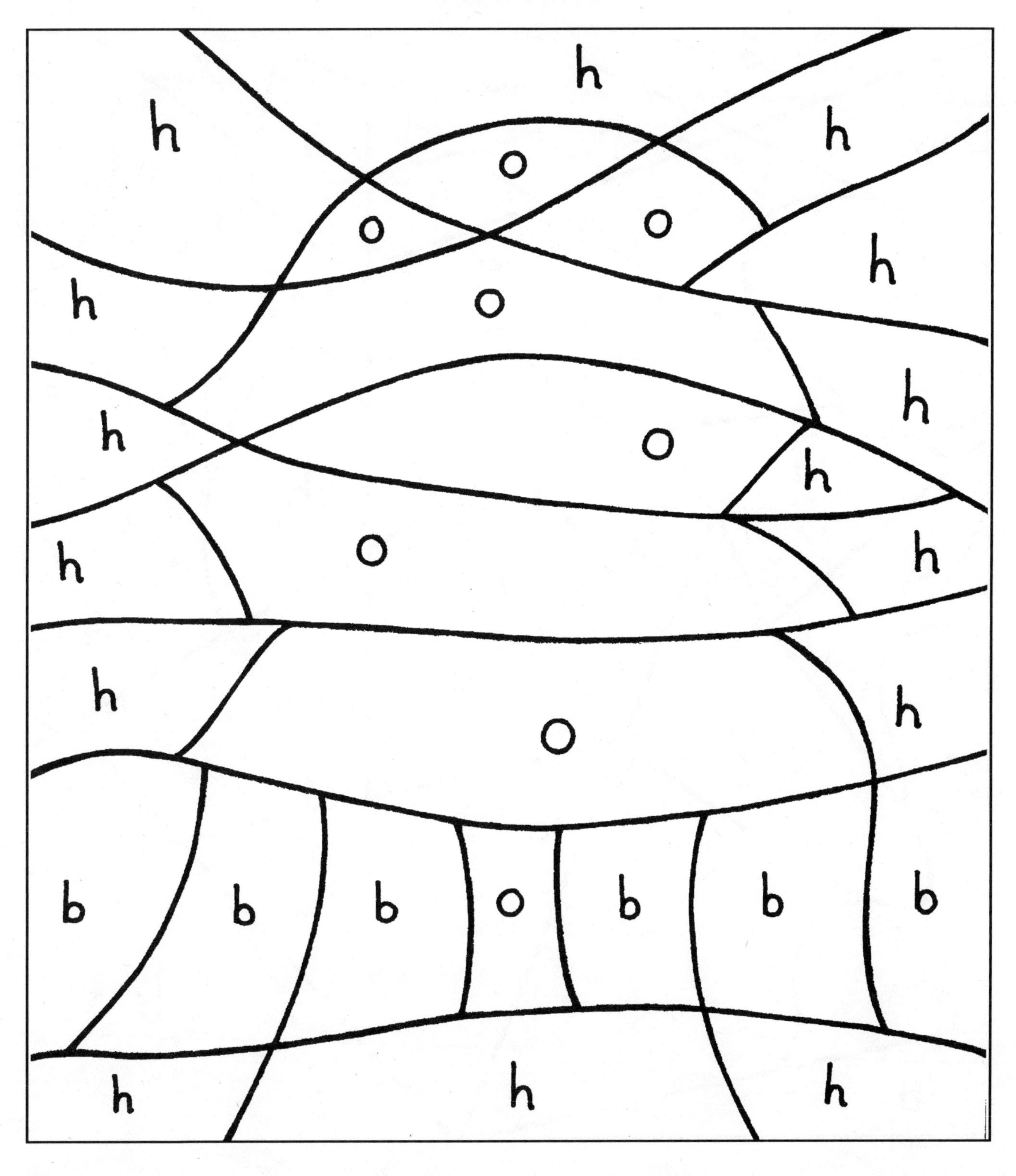

● Name ______________________

Picture this – a, w and b

Colour the a spaces red

Colour the w spaces blue

Colour the b spaces green

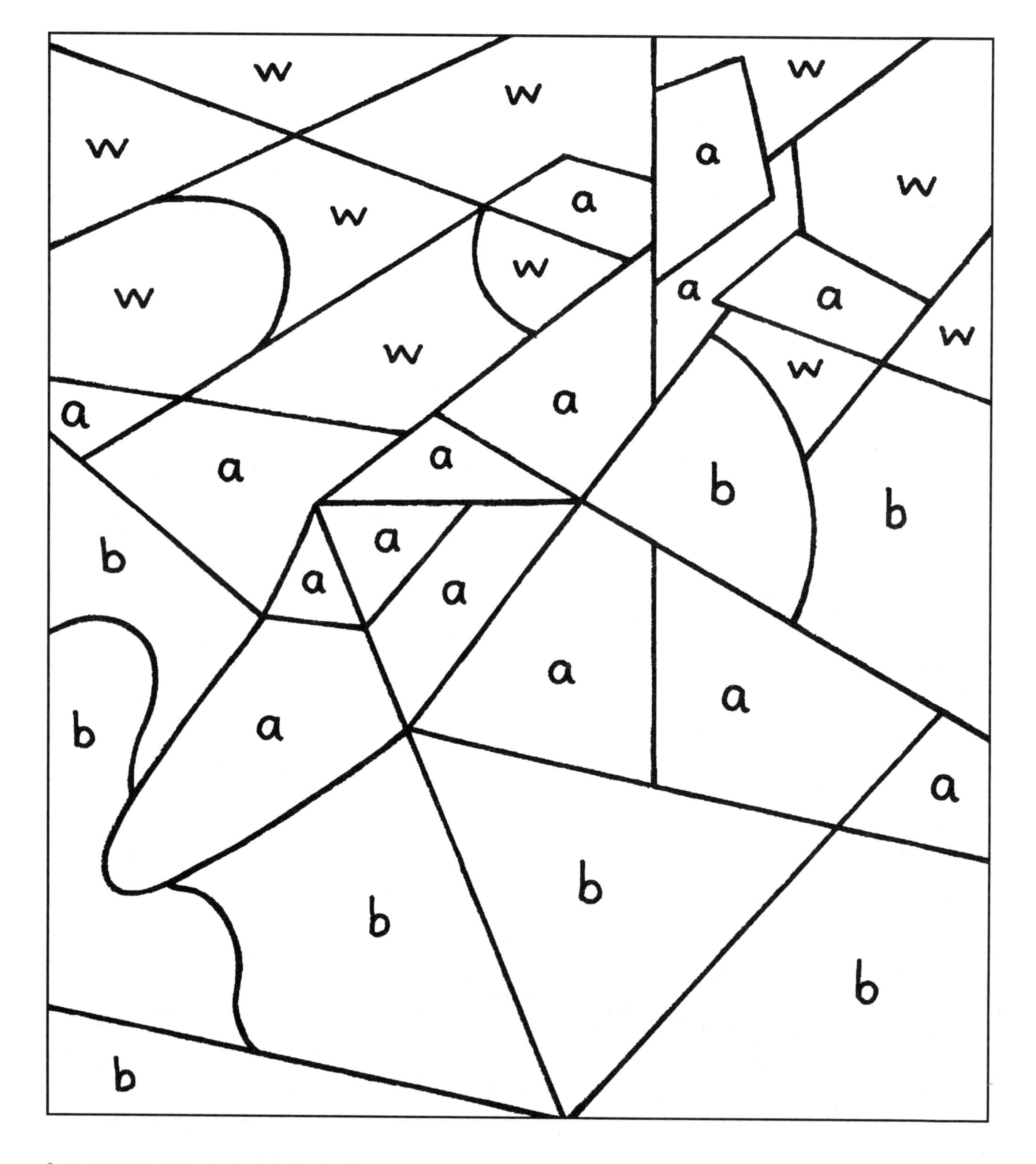

● Name ______________________

Odd one out

Cross out the letter in each flower that is the odd one out.

Colour the vase.

● Name ____________________

Pairing up – 1

Draw a ring round the two letters in each kite that are the same.

Colour the tails of the kites.

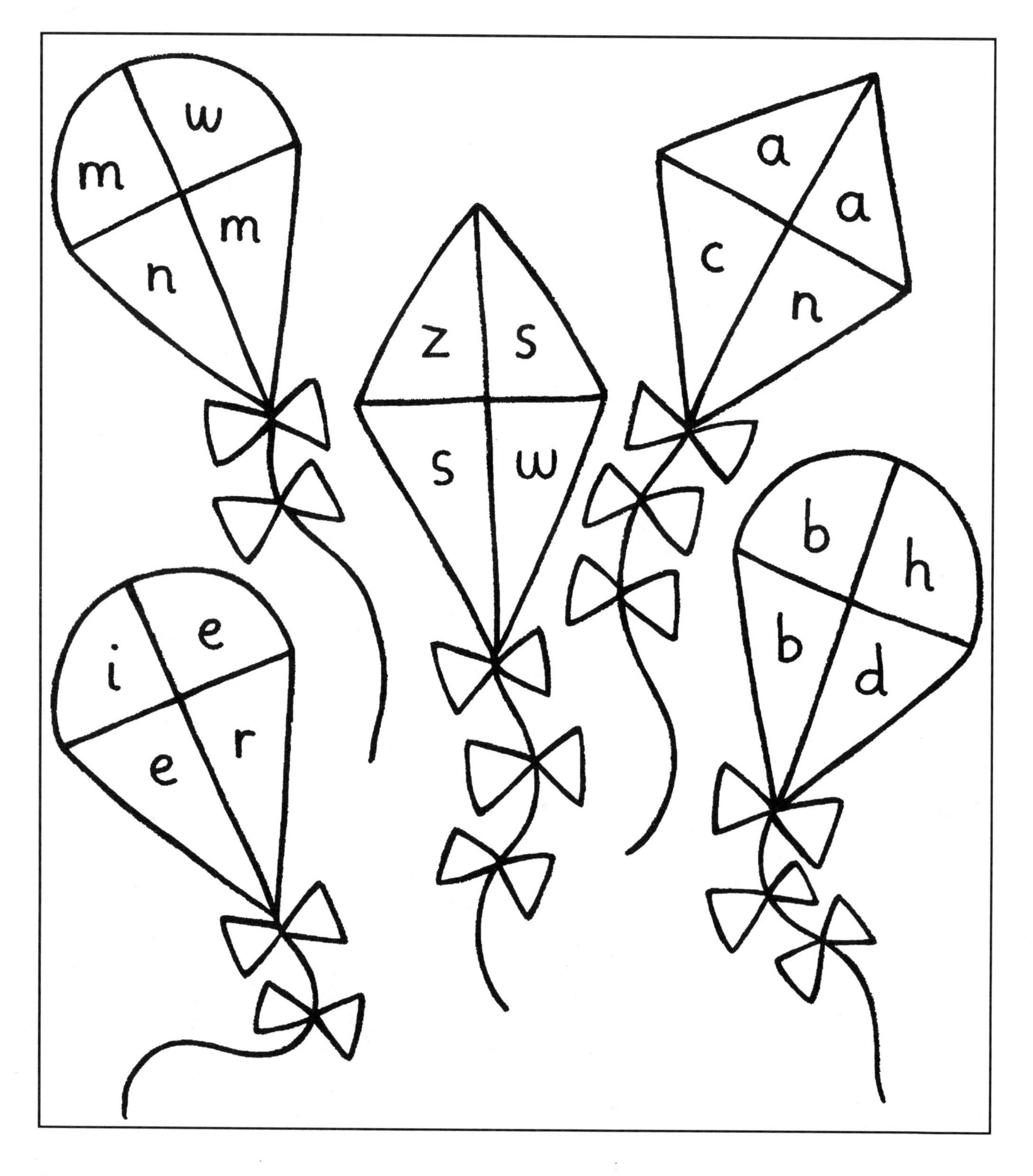

● Name ______________________

Pairing up – 2

Draw a ring round the two letters in each butterfly that are the same.

Colour the tree.

● Name ______________________

Words and pictures a to d

Write each letter. Then join the two pictures that start with that letter.

Colour the pictures.

● Name ______________________

Words and pictures e to h

Write each letter. Then join the two pictures that start with that letter.

Colour the pictures.

● Name ______________________

Words and pictures i to l

Write each letter. Then join the two pictures that start with that letter.

Colour the pictures.

● Name ______________________

Words and pictures m to p

Write each letter. Then join the two pictures that start with that letter.

Colour the pictures.

● Name ____________________________

Words and pictures q to u

Write the letter. Then join the two pictures that start with that letter.

Colour the pictures.

● Name ____________________

Words and pictures v to z

Write the letter. Then join the two pictures that start with that letter.

Colour the pictures.

● Name ______________________

Letter-to-letter a to g

Join the letters in the picture.

a b c d e f g

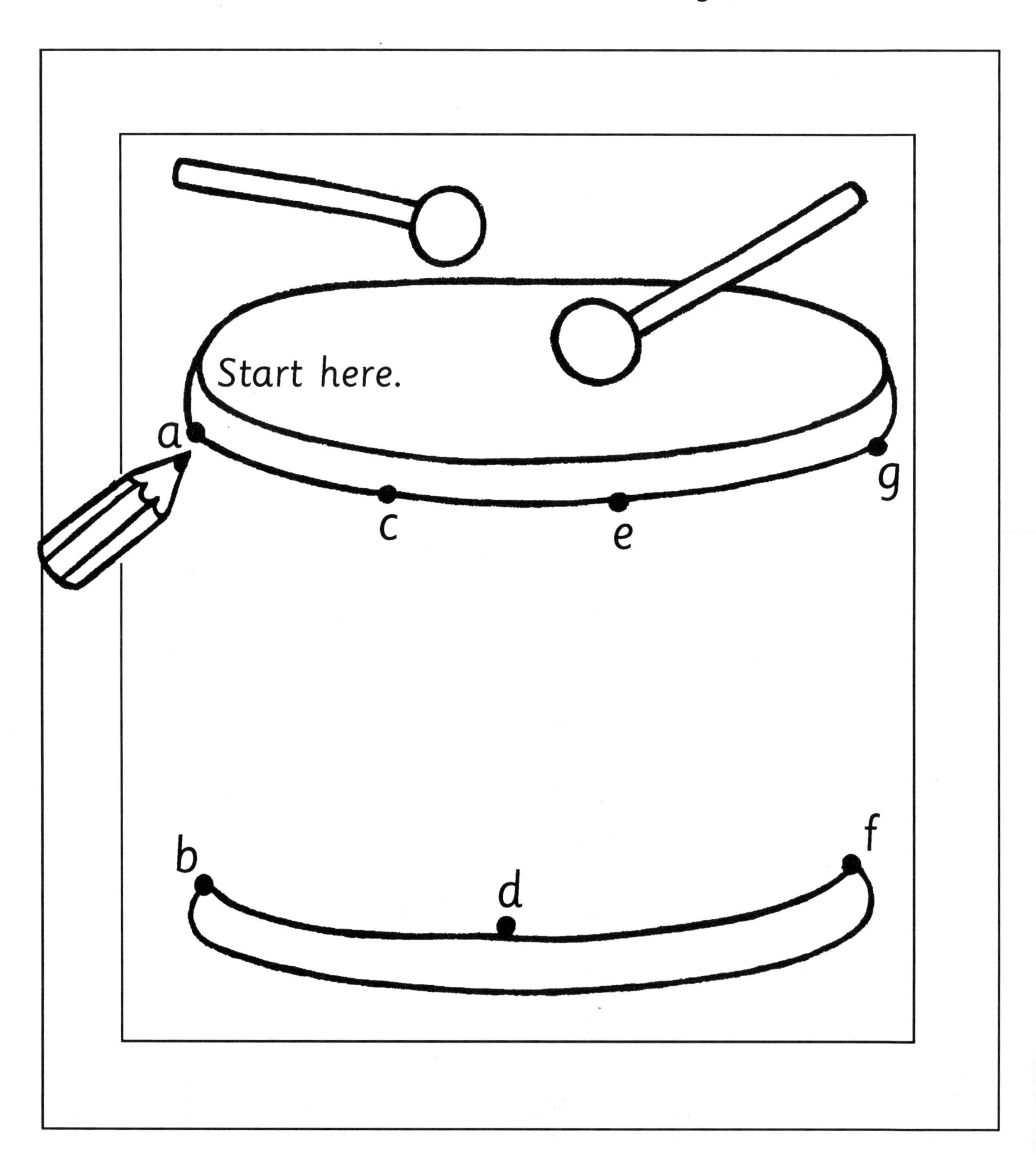

Now make a pattern in the frame.

● Name ___________________

Letter-to-letter h to m

Join the letters in the picture.

h i j k l m

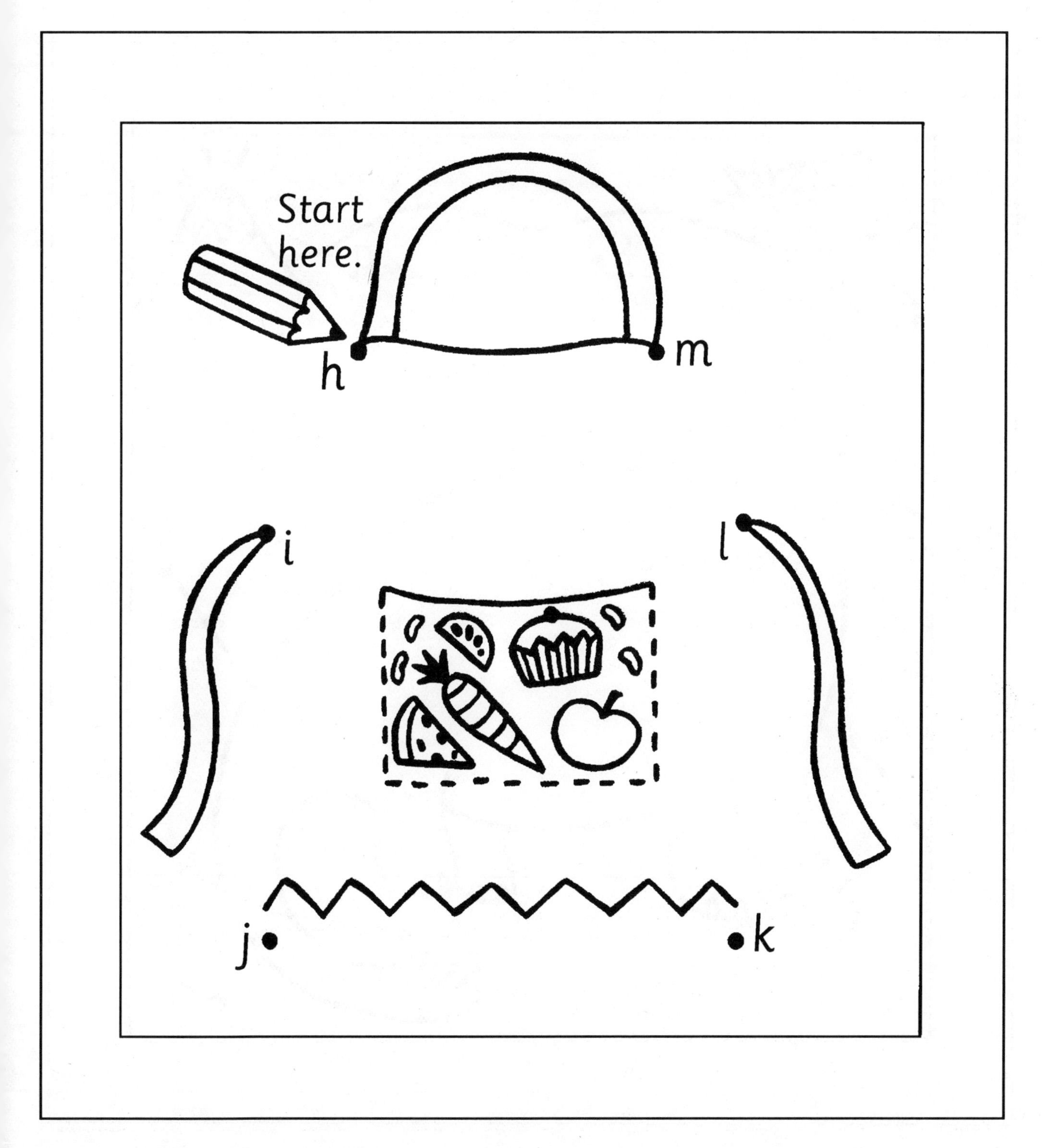

Now make a pattern in the frame.

● Name ______________________

Letter-to-letter n to u

Join the letters in the picture.

n o p q r s t u

Now make a pattern in the frame.

● Name ____________________

Letter-to-letter v to z

Join the letters in the picture.

v w x y z

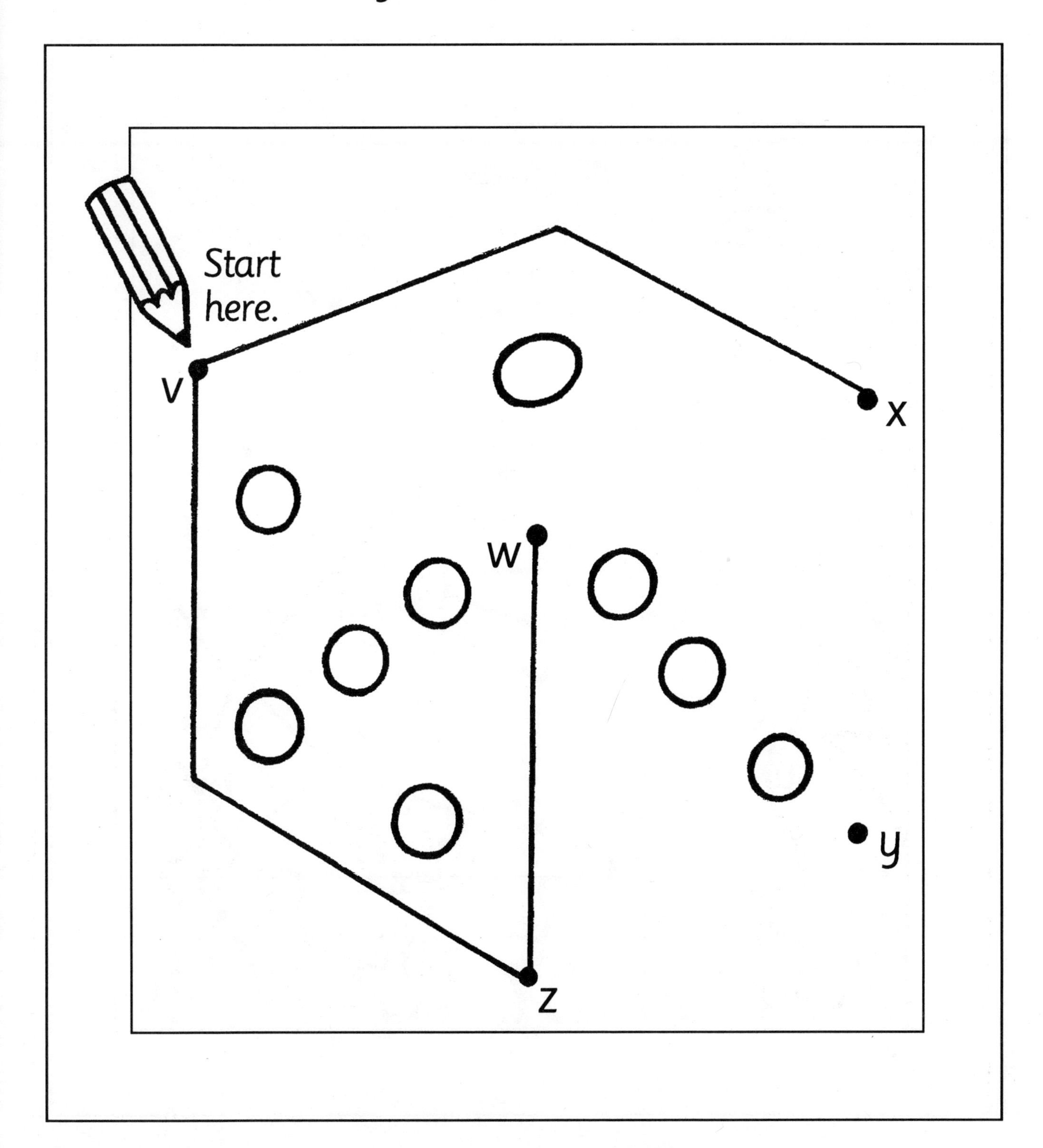

Now make a pattern in the frame.

● Name ___________________________

Letter-to-letter a to z

Join the letters in the picture.

a b c d e f g h i j k l m n o p q r s t u v w x y z

Now make a pattern in the frame.